THE Bedtime BOOK

Simple Wisdom for Children of All Ages

PAINTINGS BY N.A. NOËL

simple wisdom for children of all ages

Poetry by

Denise Daun Anderson

Diana Prince

John Wm. Sisson

Design by

Jennifer Bradley-Simmons

Some of the original paintings in this book are available as fine art prints.
For information on purchasing prints, award-winning books or to request a free Noël Studio color catalog, contact:

Noël Studio, Inc.
75 North Main Street
Zionsville, Indiana 46077
1-800-444-6635 | www.nanoel.com

THE Bedtime Book

Paintings by N. A. Noël

Poetry by
Denise Daun Anderson
Diana Prince
John Wm. Sisson

Design by Jennifer Bradley-Simmons

PRINTED IN COLLABORATION WITH

ISBN: 158209704-6

2007

THE INSPIRATION and appreciation for the art of poetry began at a very young age for me. To this day, I can recite perfectly the *Ballad of the Tempest* by James T. Fields.

My grandfather would sit with me and gently refresh my memory each summer day...until perfection. I was five years old. Today, it is not so much the *Ballad of the Tempest* that I remember with great affection, but rather my grandfather.

In an age where our technology has advanced beyond our spirituality, I hope that this little offering of collected poems may find its way into your home and your heart and bring you closer to your spirit and those you love. I dedicate *The Bedtime Book* to my grandfather, W. A. Hanley, an uncommonly wise and wonderful man, who I came to know and cherish because of the poetry we shared, and who gave me the opportunity to find my art and my spirit.

~ N.A. NOËL

About the Authors

JOHN WILLIAM SISSON

John William Sisson has a Bachelor's Degree in fine arts from Purdue University, with minors in Anthropology, Sociology and Biology. He is a descendant of the Mayflower pilgrims and has relatives who died on the Cherokee Trail of Tears. He is a Hoosier native who has nonetheless lived in such diverse places as San Francisco, Colorado, Key Largo, Tucson, and most recently, Taos, New Mexico. John is an award-winning artist, poet and professional photographer, and has taught martial arts for over 40 years. *John dedicates this book with love and affection to his two cousins, John and Earl Rich, for their unparalleled support in his work and life.*

DIANA PRINCE

Diana Prince earned a Master's Degree in English and a Master's Degree in Philosophy from San Diego State University. She completed a Doctorate in Psychology at United States International University. Diana has had over 100 poems published in poetry magazines including *Roanoke Review, Southern Poetry Review,* and *Western Review*. She published *Blackbird Spring*, a book of her poetry, and edited *WomanSoul*, a collection of work by women poets. She has had stories and articles published in *Woman's Day*, *Ingenue*, and *Aeroplane Monthly*. She taught Literature at San Diego State University and Philosophy at National University and was Feature Editor for *San Diego Celebrity Magazine*.

Diana has traveled extensively in Tibet, China, Morocco, and Antarctica. Her personal interests include traveling, skydiving, and combat aircraft. Formerly an aerospace writer, college teacher and chaplain, she now works with abused children in Southern California. *Dedication: For my mother, Katherine, who has always been the poetry in my life.*

DENISE DAUN ANDERSON

Denise Daun Anderson began writing poetry as a young child. As she became familiar with rhyming and patterns, Denise sent these treasures to her favorite grandmother for encouragement. Denise's first short story, *Sammy the Snail*, won the First Annual Christine Baer Original Story Award from Egbert W. Beach School in Piedmont, California. As Denise moved through some particularly challenging times, she became aware of a strong spiritual presence in her life. Through this awareness, she was able to perceive the divinity in all souls, and the perfection of all experiences. She was inspired to share her awareness with others through poetry, stories, and even music. One of these later works, *Song of Peace*, was published in 1989 in *The New Day Herald*, a newspaper that is sent to countries around the world.

Denise continues to focus on developing her spiritual awareness. She resides in Santa Barbara, California, and gains inspiration from her frequent travels to Maui. *Denise dedicates this book to John-Roger and John Morto, her wayshowers.*

About the Designer

JENNIFER BRADLEY-SIMMONS

Jennifer Bradley-Simmons graduated from Indiana State University with a Bachelor's Degree in Broadcast Journalism and went on to study design at the University of Indianapolis. She has been a successful designer in Indianapolis for more than 10 years and is currently the art director for Noël Studio. Her work includes many collaborative projects with Nancy Noël including the print "Spirit of Freedom." Jennifer also designs a line of greeting cards for Recycled Paper Greetings, Inc. found in Target and card stores nationwide. She is currently working on a cookbook due to print in the fall. *Dedication: For the love of my life, Steve and for our beautiful son, Alec, whose laughter and smile make every day such a gift.*

The Rabbit-Cat

IN THE WINTER IN A HOUSE
    LIVED A HAPPY LITTLE MOUSE.

But relatives and friends he made
Came that winter where he stayed.
They ate his bread and ate his cheese
And never once said thanks or please!
The humans living in the house
Didn't mind the little mouse,
But feeding family, guest or friends
In every case must have an end!
And so with all the mice around
A hungry cat must now be found!

The family searched both far and wide
To find a cat to bring inside
And clean it up and treat it nice
In hope it eats the little mice.
But don't you know, as luck would have it,
All they found, one scrawny rabbit!
And so they brought the bunny home,
Thinking maybe size alone
Would maybe kind of scare a mouse
Away from all their food and house!

The family named the rabbit "Cat"
And fed it till it got real fat!

But as that bunny grew and grew,
Every family member knew
No self-respecting mouse would fear
A cat who had that size of ear!
And so they made a little hat
To hide the ears of rabbit "Cat."
They placed the hat on rabbit's dome
To wear and scare the mice 'round home.
And hoping that was all it took,
They gave the hat a kitty look,
And though the shape was kind of rough,
They hoped that it was just enough
When placed upon the rabbit's head
Would fill the mice with fear and dread!

But then they thought that without fail
Mice would see its fluffy tail
And realize a cat-like creature
Wouldn't have this fluffy feature!

And so the family got a rope
And tied it to its tail in hope
That any mouse that it would find
Wouldn't see it from behind.
So by the time they saw its head
All the mice had run and fled!

But then the family took a pause…
Poor rabbit hadn't any claws!
And they might find among the mice
One who looked, not once but twice,

And saw the rabbit was no match.
Without its claws it couldn't catch
Any self-respecting mouse
Anywhere throughout the house!
So now the family had to make
Claws for rabbit that were fake.
And so with string and sealing wax
Onto its toes they tied some tacks.

Finally they thought rabbit ready
Even though it stood unsteady.
It looked every bit the part
To put the fear in every heart
Of all the mice that it would find
To help them have a change of mind
And move into another house
That's safe for a rat or mouse!

But it was funny, don't you know
That when they let the bunny go
It was worse than they had feared
For all the mice just stood and cheered!

The little mouse on their behalf
Thanked the family for the laugh,
But they were leaving anyhow,
They didn't like the rabbit's chow.
A self-respecting mouse was fed
A hunk of cheese or piece of bread.
No longer could the mice all bear it,
Eating lettuce or a carrot!

They knew the cat was really rabbit,
What told them was its other habit.
For all that they would rearrange
Was something humans couldn't change.
For when cat-rabbit moved around
The mice went crazy from the sound!
They moved because of bunny's hop,
They couldn't make the thumping stop!!!

So every one, no matter who
Will always have a thing they do
When added to the final mix
Helps the rest of us to fix
All the problem we all share
Just by them just being there!

—John Wm. Sisson

The Other End of the Rainbow

From the stories we've been told,
A leprechaun will bury gold

Any place the rainbows start
Though their ends are far apart!
And then one morning early dawn
A rainbow started on my lawn.
And so I knew that late that night
A leprechaun would out of sight
From the stories we've been told
Bury there a pot of gold!

So in the day I took a nap
So late that night that I might trap
A leprechaun right at the spot
Where he would bury gold and pot!
I ate my dinner, did my chores.
And after playing out of doors
I climbed in bed and under cover
In hopes of what I'd soon discover!
And after all my prayers were said
And as I listened in my bed
I thought I heard a kind of sound
Like someone digging in the ground
And so I got up from my sleep
And went outside and took a peep…

And there he was, to no surprise,
A leprechaun the kind and size
Dressed in clothes the color green
Like every picture that we've seen!
And so I hid behind a tree
Hoping that of course I'd see
How leprechauns can in a space
Bury gold without a trace!
But quiet as I tried to be
That leprechaun discovered me!
So when somehow he made a motion,
It was me that got the notion
Even though I thought I hid,
It was me I knew he bid!
And so I slowly stepped aside
From the place I tried to hide…
He softly called me by my name
When from my hiding place I came
I knew then this was no chance meeting
When I heard his kindly greeting.
And I can tell you in his suit
That leprechaun was really cute
And I could feel a kind of cheer
Full of love and free of fear
And mixed with humor, just a trace
That I could see upon his face!

So when I got up close he said,
"I'll bet you've got it in your head
That with me is a pot of gold
You can handle, count, and hold.
And when you think I'm not around
You'll dig it up from underground
And count the money in the pot
From all the gold you think you got.
But here's what I find you'll find funny,
There isn't any gold or money
At any rainbow you can bend
Of any size at either end!

The gold that we would like to share
Is if you're good, and kind, and care.
That's gold that you will always carry
And never have to hide or bury!
So you will have yourself to thank
For what you carry in your bank!
Life's not about a pot of gold
Like other stories you've been told,
But gold is how you treat a friend
Who's at your rainbow's other end!"

—John Wm. Sisson

The Tallest Smallest Tail Tale

LONG BEFORE THE SHOPPING MALL

Or the buildings standing tall,
Right upon this very spot
Whether you believe or not
A strange event had once occurred
That happened to a single bird
That changed the lives throughout the land
Right on this spot where we all stand!

And just to keep the story fair,
It's true, of course, I wasn't there.
But it's a story often told
About the smallest bird so bold
That where she goes and when she's coming
Everywhere you hear her humming.
And even though her tail's the smallest,
Her tale of all now stands the tallest.

The summer had a greenish hue,
For everything felt fresh and new.
And everywhere across the land,
Wherever all the creatures band,
There's joy and laughter all around
Because of all the food they found
Where all the children they gave birth
Can live and eat upon the earth!

The buffalo had got the word
That everyone in every herd
Must weave between a mountain pass
Into a valley full of grass
With waters in a crystal lake
Made from a dam the beavers make.
And in the valley they'll call home
Where every buffalo can roam
And always find below their feet
The grass is green and good to eat!
And so it was that through the pass
The buffalo all moved in mass.
And when they made the final tally
Every one was in that valley.
No buffalo of any kind
Of any herd was left behind
And all of them were finally able
To dine with all upon the table!

Now this may seem to stretch belief,
But all of them had just one chief.
And everywhere that elder led

The buffalo did what he said.
And so he gave a little prayer
That all the buffalo were there.
And finally the entire bunch
Could dine together every lunch!

Now by the lake there was a wood
Where once a tower of trees then stood.
And by this local wood and pool
There lived a tiny flying jewel.
And all the creatures all around
They loved her tiny little sound.
A little song that she could sing
Just by the beating of her wing.
And as she spent the morning hours
Darting through the trees and flowers,
All the creatures everywhere
Loved her humming in the air!

The beaver husband and his wife
Lived a life so free of strife
That all their children laughed and played
Upon the dam the beavers made.
And all their sons and all their daughters
Spent their youth upon the waters
That their parents' dam would stop
High upon the mountain top
While in the valley down below
Grazed all the herds of buffalo
Who with the creatures in the wood
Always knew they always could

Along a path and in a link
Altogether get a drink!

They knew the beavers like to share
The waters they have stored up there.
But beaver with his wise advice
Said, "Treat the water very nice
For we have built the only source
For every buffalo and horse,
For deer, and duck, and all the moose
And fish and frogs and swan and goose,
The cougar, wolf, and even bear
Will go to get a drink up there.
And if by chance the dam should break
Think of all the mess it'd make!"
So every creature understood
Throughout the valley and the wood
That dam was built of limbs and mud
And if it broke they'd have a flood
That only those who would survive
Are those who could swim out alive.

And so it was for many years
They lived a life so free of fears
That everyone began to think
The lake was their own private sink
And did not take the time or care
To help the beavers to repair
The damaged dam they all had caused
With hooves and feet and fins and claws!

And so a tiny leak was sprung
And missed by all except for one
Who with her tiny little beak
Plugged the hole and stopped the leak.
And with her wings she made a hum
That told the others all to come
To help her with a helping hand
To save them all and spare the land
From all the water and the mud
Her beak was saving from a flood!
For hummingbird, that tiny jewel
Had never been that big a fool.
She may be small but she would know
How big a little thing can grow!
The beavers found the jewel stuck
Amongst the limbs and all the muck.
But when they pulled her from the leak
The beavers kind of stretched her beak.
But even though her beak was long
It didn't change her humming song!
So hummingbird had saved the day
Where all the creatures eat and play.
And no one would have ever heard
Of buffalos without that bird.
So even though her tail was smallest
Her tale of all became the tallest!

—John Wm. Sisson

Have to Get to a Different Day

THERE ARE MANY THINGS I "HAVE" TO DO,
OR SO I USED TO THINK!

Wash the dishes, mop the floor,
And clean the kitchen sink.

But then one day I came to find
It wasn't quite that way,
And if you turn the coin around
You'll have a different day.

Instead of saying how a job
Is really just a chore,
Change a word and you will find
A way to do much more!

It's really not about the fact
There's things you "have" to do,
But others that you'll never know
Would like to be like you!

They'd like to "have" a kitchen sink,
Or even "have" a dish,
Let alone a mop and floor
To wash each time they wish.

Next time you "have" a thing to do,
Don't moan and be upset,
But change the word of "have" around
And use the word I "get!"

I "get" to do so many things
That others wish they could,
What once I thought I had to do
I "get" to now do good!

It's not about the things we "have"
Or what we "have" to do,
It's how we look at life itself
And what's inside of you.

For if you turn those words around
To find that other way,
I guarantee that you will see
You'll "get" that different day!

—John Wm. Sisson

Angel Leases

WHEN YOU'RE SAD
AND FEELING DOWN,

That's when a friend will come around
And find the things that make you blue
And then remind you why you're you,
That you're the one they came to see,
How better could a friendship be!

All the ups and downs you share,
Friends, of course, are always there.

Trials life can put you through
Show you when a friend is true.
And when in life you're having fun,
You know you're not the only one.
A friend who truly in their heart
Loves you from the very start
Will always be there in the end
Friends are angels on the lend!

—*John Wm. Sisson*

What Momma Said!

I REMEMBER MOMMA SAID
IF I REALLY USED MY HEAD,

I could be the President
And then the places that we went
We could arrive at every scene
In my official limousine.
And as she stepped out of my car
Looking like a movie star,
They would strike up all the bands
As Momma waved to all her fans,
Even though the place we went
They came to see the President!

Momma always made up stories
Made from past and present glories
Of the wizards and the elves,
Stories not upon my shelves,
Of lands that she would take me to
And not a single word was true!
For everything my Momma said
Were stories made up in her head.

At least that's what I thought before
That stranger knocked on Momma's door!
But never, ever, anyplace
Have I seen his kind of face.
For when I took his coat and hat,
There he stood, a six-foot rat!
And I admit I couldn't help
As I let out a wild yelp

And nearly fainted to the floor,
For who she let inside our door!

But then I heard my Momma say,
"It's sweet of you to come this way!
I haven't seen you way since when
I sent you there, you're back again!"

Then that rat got on his knees
And said, "My queen, forgive me please,
For when you sent me on my chores
To far off lands and distant shores
It took me longer than I thought
To bring to you the thing I brought!"

And then he gave a little tug
To what he placed upon the rug,
And from a sack a golden box
Appeared with chains and silver locks!
Then he placed upon her knee
A tiny, shiny crystal key
And said, "My lady, I regret
The wizard hasn't come here yet.
But he sent me ahead to say
That he was now upon his way!"

I'm sure that you could feel my shock
When there it came, another knock!

And there he stood, a six-food lizard
Dressed exactly like a wizard!
Then quicker than a summer storm
That lizard changed to human form!
And he could tell by my surprise
I thought my Momma's stories lies.
And as he helped me from the floor,
Another knock came to our door!

So now I'm fully wide awake
But don't know how much I can take
Of any more of Momma's friends
Who've come to bow and make amends
Before my Momma, who they seem
To somehow think my Momma's queen!
Yet there he was, and with his log,
A green, but handsome giant frog!

And right behind there came the elf,
Who didn't come here by himself.
So trust me, there was no relief
When in there walked a goblin chief!
If beauty's in the eye, they say,
That goblin's seen a better day!
For though he walked as if a man,
His face looked like a garbage can!
I know I'm not the one to judge,
But with a face like slime and sludge
I thought our garbage in our drive
Had if by magic come alive!

But when I heard what goblin spoke,
I knew for him it was no joke.

For that old goblin thought it best
That what was in the golden chest
Should stay inside and there remain,
Or none of them would stay the same!
And I could see there just a trace
Of worry on that goblin's face.

And then my Momma, with a frown,
Asked them all to please sit down.
But not, of course, the handsome frog,
Who squatted down upon his log!

And so they had a trial of sort
And used our dining room as court
And asked my Momma one by one
What she thought that should be done
With the thing within the box
Held with chains and silver locks!

The wizard thought it also best
That they never try to test
What was under lock and key
Because of what the price might be,
For all the secrets you would hear
Might overnight just disappear
And all the tales that we all trust
Might overnight return to dust!

The handsome frog then spoke his piece
And said," We never should release
A single lock or single chain
For in that box it should remain
And never let it get away

Or we will all regret this day,
For many things that we hold dear
Are going to be destroyed, I fear!"
And then the elf said, "Keep it hid
And put a rock upon the lid
The size of a gigantic ox
So nothing gets outside that box
For if it does, then all of you
Will also disappear from view!"

And so it was in all this drama
Everyone turned toward my Momma
And begged her in a single voice
How they felt about the choice
To open up the lock and key
And let it all go wander free.
But they would do what Momma said
Despite the trouble up ahead
And though they'd rather keep it hid
They all would do what Momma bid!

I've got to say, I must confess
That I was now a total mess.
But I could never let it show
Or all the other folks would know
What I thought were Momma's lies
Were sitting there to my surprise
Debating what was in a box
Wrapped in chains with silver locks!

Then I heard my Momma say,
"Thanks for coming all this way.
From each of you I truly heard

Every heartfelt single word.
And so it is my own decree
That we must let this matter be!
I think for all it would be best
That if we leave within the chest
The one thing, if the truth be told,
Would ruin us for young and old!"

So there it was, they went away,
But now I know they will some day
Return to Momma…oops, I mean
Her royal majesty, the queen!
So now a tale your Momma tells
About the goblins or her spells
You just might want to think again
About her friends she knew back then,
For once upon a time, it's true,
I used to wonder just like you,
But now I've seen them for myself,
A wizard, goblin, frog, and elf,
And now I know what Momma did
By keeping that box closed and hid!

She saved the world a lot of harm
By keeping just a little charm
In all the tales that parents tell
To weave their secret magic spell!
The thing my Momma won't let out
Was in that box a "little doubt!"

—John Wm. Sisson

Songs in the Night

WHEN THE EVENING SUN GOES DOWN
THINGS GET QUIET IN OUR TOWN.

But on the edge and in the forest
You should hear the nightly chorus
Away from your own house and bed
In places city-dwellers dread
Because they find the only light
Comes from the moon and stars at night.
While many hear the barking dog,
Most will miss the big bullfrog
Because the only sounds he'll make
Are in a pond or by a lake.
But when he's safe and in his place
You should hear his booming bass
Booming like a big bass drum
While all around mosquitoes hum.
Of course you'll hear in every thicket
The chirps and fiddles of the cricket.
And in the forest further still
You'll hear the songs of whip-poor-will.
And further yet the coyotes howl,
Joined there by the hoots of owl
While in the air and crystal clear
The bats sing songs you'll never hear.

It may be quiet on your street,
But not where all the critters meet.
Some of them can't sing a tune,
Like possums, mice, and most raccoon,
Or neither can a bunch of bugs,
Like moths, and snails, and slimy slugs.
But all of them come out at dark
To hear the chorus in their park.
And some of them are treated nice,
But others pay a heavy price.
Although they say the music's fine,
It's played where all the critters dine
And in the middle of a song
Sometimes some things go very wrong.
And though they try their very best
To sing out louder than the rest,
You'll hear them choke that final note
As if they're caught in someone's throat!

—John Wm. Sisson

Twice Upon a Time Ago

TWICE UPON A TIME AGO

Something happened you all know.
A prince was sitting on a log
Who had a face just like a frog!
And yes, he was a little green,
His body squat, his legs were lean,
And even though he had a hump,
Wow, that prince could really jump!
His eyes would kind of bulge a bit,
And you could laugh at how he'd sit.
And when the prince was very young
He did catch flies, but with his tongue!

The king and queen were very fond
Of their son out in his pond!
They knew before but never since
Had any maiden kissed a prince
She didn't know nor hadn't seen,
Especially one who's kind of green!

You see, the king had been a frog
The queen had found upon a log.
For she's the one who did it first,
To kiss a frog a witch had cursed!
But no one else had ever since
Kissed a frog that was a prince…
The queen had known when he was born
And had a kind of tadpole form,
Her son, the princely pollywog,
Might one day call his throne a log.

So even though it made her sad,
The same thing happened to his dad.
And so she thought that given time,
That in their search they too might find
That somewhere there's another one
Just dumb enough to kiss her son!
For who would walk through swamps and bogs
To find a prince by kissing frogs?

And after several years went by
They found some maidens they would try.
But every time they saw their son,
They'd yell and scream and try to run!
So every time he was rejected
Made the prince just more dejected.

The king then said, "It's all my fault!"
And brought the process to a halt.
You see, his father understood
The problems of his bachelorhood.

The king knew maidens like to marry
Someone warm and kind of hairy.
Cold and green weren't really in
To snuggle up against your skin.
And so he bought his son a coat
To keep him warm out in the moat.
But when the prince would try to swim

It very soon occurred to him
That in his coat the prince had found
A furry coat could make him drown
Out in his pond or any lake
And that would be a big mistake!
His coat became a soggy sack
And so he wisely gave it back.

The queen said, "King, it's now my turn!
From your example I can learn
The only way to help our son
Become the prince he might become.
Put all the maidens to the test!
Invite them all to be our guest!
And everyone shall kiss the prince,
Even if they scream and wince
To make the spell go in reverse
And help our prince remove this curse!"

And so the king with wave of hand
Gathered maids throughout the land.
And even though they might resist,
All of them would all get kissed!
But in the end it would convince
There was no maid to help the prince.

And so they finally faced the truth
That they had known and since his youth

That though they had a cat and dog,
They also had a son, a frog!
For it should come as no surprise
When with his tongue he's catching flies!

But then one day another frog
Found the pond and saw the log.
And soon the prince came swimming by
And then they caught each other's eye.
And that was it, that's all it took,
They fell in love with just one look!

Soon the wedding day was planned
And all would come throughout the land!
But many came in all green suits,
Lizards, turtles, toads, and newts!
They wished the frogs the very best
Both in the pond and on the nest!

The king and queen were very proud
At all the turnout of the crowd,
For king and queen both understood
That really for their son's own good
They finally had to both be seen
Embracing those the color green!

—John Wm. Sisson

See My Horse?

WHAT DO YOU THINK MOST FOLKS WOULD FEEL

About a horse that wasn't real?
I've got a horse no one can see
That everywhere will follow me!

Like when I go to any store
That horse will beat me to the door,
And up and down in every aisle
That horse will prance in princely style.
But how he does it I can't guess
For never has he made a mess.
You'd think that prancing by itself
Would knock just one thing off a shelf!

And when we're going to the zoo,
You should see the things he'll do.
He visits every creature there,
Zebra, penguin, beaver, bear,
And all of them it seems, of course,
Can also see my friend the horse.
So every creature he walks by
Will always turn to tell him hi.
And everybody thinks it's me
That all those critters turn to see.
I swear to them I'm not the source,
But no one else can see the horse!

Sometimes when we're both in the park,
And just before it's getting dark
I see him do his favorite thing

And get on board the biggest swing
And there he'll neigh a little song
Until the sun is finally gone!

Usually he has just one rule
That when he's waiting after school
He never goes aboard the bus
To cause a riot or a fuss.
He goes along and for a ride
By running by the bus's side!
But no one else in any seat
Can see that horse out on the street.
And by the time we're rounding home,
I'm in my seat, but all alone,
The other riders moving clear
Because of how I yell and cheer
At races none of them can see
Between that bus and horse for me!

We often played a little game
Where I would try to guess his name,
And if one day I got it right
The horse would disappear from sight!

So in the time the game would take
I'd always make the same mistake,
Because I had a dreadful fear
The horse would really disappear
And I might find that in the end

I'd won the game but lost a friend!
Just so that horse would never leave,
I'd always guess his name was Steve!

Once one Christmas in the snow
That horse had gone where I won't go!
He jumped upon my neighbor's roof
And in the snow and with his hoof
He made some footprints like a deer
To make them think that Santa's here!

And there I stood, no place to hide,
Wrapped in my coat, it's cold outside.
And don't you know it, as I feared,
My neighbors at the door appeared!

Escape for me is quite remote,
I'm caught there in my winter coat
And trying quiet as a mouse
To get a horse from off their house!

Another summer I recall,
Or was it spring or maybe fall,
That horse and I went for a hike.
He trotted as I rode my bike
And teased me that I wasn't fast
And in a race I'd never last.
And just to see who'd win the most
He'd race with me from coast to coast!
But just to make an even start,
I rode my bike, he used a cart.
So in the race upon the course
I put the cart before the horse!

So we had raced about a mile
When I could see that horse's smile.
I heard him say, "Around that bend
I'd like to try the other end
For if we're going very far
I'd like to see just where we are.
And from this end the cart I'd say
In front of me is in my way."

And so I turned the cart around,
But even so the horse had found
That with that cart still in his face
That horse was winning second place!

My friends all told me, think it over
And maybe get a dog named Rover,
And maybe give my brain a test
And let my "horsey" have a rest
Because they said no ifs or buts,
To see a horse I must be nuts,
Especially one they couldn't see!
Which made it very bad for me,
For if I really had to choose,
It could be all my friends I lose!

I pitied them for what they lack
And climbed on board my horse's back
And sadly looked in all their eyes
So full of wonder and surprise
As I rode off upon that horse…
The one they couldn't see, of course!

—John Wm. Sisson

The Wooden Angel

Some say that I
just made this up,

While others know the truth,
It happened to a friend of ours
When we were in our youth.

While other boys were playing war
With guns and toy tanks,
Michael always walked away
And always said, "No thanks."
He really didn't care for war,
He didn't like to fight,
He thought there must be other ways
To somehow make things right!

While other boys had larger toys
Like a train or toy rocket,
Michael treasured just one toy
He carried in his pocket.
And every day he went to play
When no one was about,
Then Michael in a secret place
Would bring his one toy out
And place there on a little rock
An angel carved in wood,
And some might call the carving crude
While others think it good!

But Michael didn't really care
What other people thought,
He had a toy like no one else
That wasn't sold or bought.
His Grampa cut it from a tree
Where Michael had a swing,
A tree that Michael loved to watch
Come back to leaf each spring.

But then one night the lightning struck,
The tree fell to the ground,
And Grampa carved a little piece
For him to carry around.
So everywhere that Michael went
His Grampa always knew
An angel from their special tree
Would always be there, too!

When he and Grampa took a walk
On paths through woods and field,
Grampa always found the things
That nature kept concealed.
And Michael learned about the frog,
He heard the tale of snake,
Stories of the bugs and birds,
And all the sounds they make!

Grampa showed him things unseen,
Like the talent of the deer

That how by simply standing still
They simply disappear.
He showed him how a rabbit's hole
Outwits the smartest fox,
And how the turtle stays alive
By living in a box.
Grampa knew the shape and size
Of every single creature,
Fins and wings and legs and things,
And every other feature!
He knew how high the eagle flew,
How fast a tree would grow,
Nothing lived or grew on earth
That Grampa didn't know!
At least that's how young Michael felt
As he looked through his eyes,
For every day of Grampa's life
Was colored by surprise!

And then one day, just like the tree,
His Grampa passed away…
No longer would the two of them
Walk in the woods to play.

Michael reached his secret spot
In a gentle, misty rain,
Knowing that the gathered clouds
Must also share his pain.
And when he found his sacred place
With the angel Grampa made,
He put her on the little rock,
And then he knelt and prayed.

"Dear God in heaven, tell my Gramps
I love him very much,
I miss his hug and great big smile,
I miss his gentle touch.
But he told me the stars I see
Are angels in the sky,
Who just like him will never dim
Their twinkle in my eye.
And so I ask you, please dear lord,
Tell Grampa I'll be good,
And thank him for my special gift,
My angel made of wood."

But then a strange thing happened,
And that angel moved its wing!
And softly in a whispered voice
Young Michael heard it sing…
"We know how much you loved your Gramps
And all the things you shared,
And all the time you spent with him
To show how much you cared.
But you should know that everywhere
Your Grampa's still alive:
He lives within your heart and mind,
His memories still survive.
Those secret tales about the woods
And how the flowers grew,
All the things that Grampa taught
You thought he never knew.
And so he carved me out of wood
With love and tender pride
To let you know that where you go
He's the angel by your side!"

—John Wm. Sisson

Heartsongs

EVERY TIME THE ANGELS SING,
THINK OF ALL THE JOY THEY BRING

Everyone across the land,
People everywhere they stand.
Even those across the sea
Hear angels in their hearts like me.
So when I think of those I love
I hear their voices from above
In songs so full and crystal clear
But in my heart, not in my ear
Where down inside beneath my skin
I feel their love so deep within
And know their chorus, every part,
Their songs of love within my heart!

—*John Wm. Sisson*

Where Angels Hid

SWEET SARA WAS A SPECIAL CHILD,
SHE HAD THIS SPECIAL GIFT,

And everyone who Sara met,
They felt their spirit lift.
And everywhere that Sara went,
And everything she did,
She always thought that good somehow
Was where the angels hid!

She always helped with morning chores,
She liked the barn the best,
She fed the chickens, milked the cow,
Picked eggs from every nest!

But Sara had a special friend
Whose coat was her pajama,
Woven from the silky hair
Of Sara's best friend...Llama!

As Sara brushed her Llama's coat,
They always had a talk
About the things they saw and heard
Each time they took a walk.
They often wandered in the fields
And passed the pond and wood
Where all the trees and flowers grew
And everything seemed good!

But then one day and in their way
A simple thing took place,
A little bird they softly heard
Was Sara's saving grace.
For there it was upon the path,
A bird with broken wing,
It couldn't fly, it couldn't walk,
And barely could it sing.
And Sara knew if left alone
The bird would not survive,
She knew she was the only chance
It had to stay alive!

So Sara with her special gift
Knew how the bird would feel.
She calmed its fear, picked it up
And said, "I'll help you heal!"

She placed the bird on Llama's back
That through the open field
Safely hid in Llama's coat
The bird would stay concealed
So neither Fox nor Mr. Owl
Nor Hawk up in the air
Would see the bird with broken wing
In Llama's silky hair!

And when they safely made it home
She fixed the broken wing,
And soon within a day or two
The bird began to sing.

And not before nor evermore
In all of Sara's years
Would she or Llama ever hear
More beauty fill their ears!

And then one day it finally came,
They had to say goodbye
And let their friend the bird take wing
Its freedom in the sky!

The bird who had the broken wing
Now fluttered from her hand,
Its wing that once before was sore
Was soaring over land!

But then a wondrous thing took place
When right before their eyes…
The bird that they both loved and saved
Was an angel in disguise!

She said, "Sweet Sara, by your act
Our love will never part,
And now you know that where we hide
Is deep within the heart.
And every time you help another
To make their dreams come true,
Know the good you feel inside
Is the angel inside you!"

—John Wm. Sisson

Shadow

IN THE SPRINGTIME

After all the showers,
I see my little shadow
Run behind me through the flowers.

And in the summer
In the long green grass,
When I whirl around so quickly
I can see him quickly pass.

In the autumn stillness
While birds sleep in the eaves,
I think sometimes I hear him
Run behind me in the leaves.

And in the wintertime
When icy breezes blow,
I see my little shadow
Run behind me in the snow.

— Diana Prince

Moon Vision

I SAW THE LOVELY
MOON TAKE FLIGHT

Across the western sky at night,
Watched quiet as it passed me by,
A silver track across the sky.

It gleamed across the garden pass,
The bright stones glittering like glass,
And traveled down the garden walk,
Past daffodils and hollyhocks.

And past the home of sleeping bees,
It stopped to linger in the trees.
And as its brilliant light rose higher
It seemed to set the leaves afire.

Above the gate's high iron bars
A thousand children called the stars
Danced round to make a silver ring;
A thousand stars began to sing.

— Diana Prince

Museum Visit

A PETRIFIED FOREST

And leaf-pointed stones,
Old Indian baskets
And dinosaur bones.

Weapons and war masks
From long fighting trips,
And delicate laces
From old Spanish ships.

Beads and bandanas
From old gypsy camps,
Statues and coins
And bright Chinese lamps.

The world is so big,
This is simply the door
To wonderful places
To love and explore.

— Diana Prince

Rainy Day

LITTLE SAMMY
COMES TO PLAY

With toys and trucks and trains.
And he brings his brand-new bike,
And his model planes.

We have lots of books to read
And lots of games to play,
And watercolor colorbooks
To pass the time away.

And with a world of things to do,
And toys set all around,
We sit against the window-glass
And watch the rain come down.

— Diana Prince

Tea Time

I LIKE TO SIT
WITH MAMA

And have a cup of tea,
Like the English people do
Each day across the sea.

All stiff and prim and proper,
Everyday at three,
We have our tea and cakes
Like they do across the sea.

I think of English ladies
When the table's set for tea,
And I wonder do they think of us
Everyday at three.

—*Diana Prince*

Jenny

SHE'S NOT THE BEST-DRESSED

But she's very polite,
And she's there if you need her
By day or by night.

And she likes to go riding
Down by the sea,
Or spend a nice day
Having hot pies and tea.

She never tells secrets
And never tells lies,
And listens so calmly
With beautiful eyes.

She sits and she smiles
From her favorite old chair,
And never goes hiding
When you leave her there.

She isn't concerned
With high-fashion at all,
But Jenny's the world's
Most wonderful doll.

— *Diana Prince*

Sand Castle

I THOUGHT I OWNED
THE CASTLE

So stately on the beach.
I built a wall and moat around
To keep it out of reach.

I put in little windows
Up in the highest towers,
And made some pink and purple shells
A garden full of flowers.

I watched the ocean rolling
Its sudden silver track
Up to my stately castle wall
And timidly roll back.

Now that the place was ocean-safe,
I hurried gladly home
To think about the castle
Circled round with sand and foam.

Nobody's kingdom but my own,
This castle by the sea,
Until next day a portly crab
Crawled out to stare at me.

And so I watched him claim
My lovely property —
This castle-creature watching
In that kingdom by the sea.

— Diana Prince

When We Grow Up

ELSIE WILL
BE A DOCTOR,

And John will be a cook.
And Bill will go to London
And Ann will write a book.

And Ted will be a painter
And Sue will fix up cars,
And Frank will use a telescope
To study all the stars.

Eileen will be a pilot
And fly a silver jet,
And me? There are so many things,
I can't decide just yet.

— Diana Prince

The Magic Lamp

MRS. BENGIE
BOUGHT A LAMP

And found a Magic Genie –
Two feet high from head to toe,
A greet suit and a beanie.

Said Mrs. Bengie, quite perturbed,
"You really ought to find
A lamp more suited to your taste,
And kindly vacate mine."

The Genie bowed a gracious bow,
"My woman, you must know,
I took up residence in here
Two thousand years ago.

So please unhand this shiny lamp,
Stop tapping like a mouse.
And if you wouldn't mind, please,
Take your fingers off my house."

— Diana Prince

The Voyage

WHEN I GROW UP
I'LL TAKE MY BOAT

To see the world
And set afloat

Toward Scotland where
The bagpipes play;
And stop in Ireland
For a day,

And wish upon
The Blarney Stone
To have a castle
For my own.

In Holland
Where the tulips lie,
The windmills spin
Against the sky.

And flowers bloom
In reds and blues
Amid the tap
Of wooden shoes.

In China
Where the Yangtze spans
The dusty roads
Of caravans,

At sunset
Down the river float
The silhouettes
Of dragon boats.

And in Old Greece
Where temples stand
Like golden pillars
On the land

I'll stand upon
The mountaintop
And wish and wish
And never stop.

This world spread out
So large, so free,
Before my little boat
And me.

— Diana Prince

Golden Windows

He sat atop the roof and saw

The blazing from the castle walls,
So far away through woods and cold,
And knew they must be made of gold.

And in his heart he loved so much
These windows that he longed to touch.
He sat and watched them from his town
Each night before the sun went down.

And how he wished that he might hold
Such shining windows made of gold.

And after years, it came to pass.
He left his hut with panes of glass.
And so he packed his little sack
With beans and bread, not looking back.
And moved as silent dusk came down
To the far corners of the town.

And with his dog he traveled days
Through leafy forest with the haze
From morning when the dewdrops fall,
Till sunset when the night birds call.

He finally felt his own heart race
When he had reached that special place.

The castle languished on the hill,
A giant fortress, and he thrilled
To touch those windows that he knew
Would gleam in brilliant golden hues.

He longed to touch the quiet cold
Soft shining of that window gold.

But when he climbed the castle pass,
He gazed on windows made of glass.
And his own eyes then lost the gleam
That fled and vanished with his dream.

As sun set high above the dome,
He longingly looked toward his home.
His simple hut was miles away
Upon the hill at end of day.

And as sun traveled up the sky,
He gasped aloud in great surprise.
He saw his small hut through the haze,
And all the windows were ablaze.

And now he knew that treasures rare
Of real gold were gathered there.
This gold he never saw before
When he was standing at his door.

And even now when sunlight spills
Into the quiet of those hills,
Around his home when winter snow
Still comes to set the world aglow,

The beauty near-at-hand remains –
His golden glow of windowpanes.

— *Diana Prince*

Halloween Night

BLACK CATS GO WALKING

On little cat feet,
Bags rustle with candy
And ghosts fill the street.

A warm pumpkin smiles
Behind window-glass
As goblins and cowboys
And tigers go past.

Witches in wigs walk in twos,
Walk in fours,
The glad trick-or-treaters
Come knocking on doors.

Tonight we become
Anyone, anything –
A princess, a clown,
A frog or a king.

To be what we wish,
And to make it come true,
What Halloween magic
To use all year through!

— Diana Prince

Searching for Me

Dear God, grant me the wisdom

To pray on bended knee
For your gentle, loving guidance
As I seek the one called Me.

I've searched throughout my lifetime
For the answers hidden well,
I've peeked in darkened corners
And in depths of fiery hell.

My journey's been a struggle
Through terrors large and small,
The darkness weaves its magic
And I heed its siren's call.

Like a moth to flame I'm often drawn
To things that cause me pain,
Oh God, I'm tired of hurting,
Has my search been all in vain?

I want so much to find her
And to hold her to my breast,
To let her know she'll always be
The one that I love best.

Sometimes I sense her presence
As though she's very near,
But the only way to find her
Is to face the things I fear.

Please light the way into my heart
And maybe there I'll see
Your precious, most beloved child,
The one that I call Me.

— *Denise Daun Anderson*

Full Circle

When I began
my journey

I chose a place to start
That's buried deep inside me,
Within my secret heart.

The trip was rarely easy,
For the path I trod was rough;
Life's thorny bushes pricked me,
And I felt like giving up.

And when I'd walked forever
Over flat and barren land;
I came onto a mountain -
My test was now at hand.

Despair became my comrade,
And I cried for most the day;
But in the end I acquiesced -
There was no other way.

With waning strength I started up
The steep and rocky slope;
I set my sights above me,
Trying never to lose hope.

And when at last I'd scaled its peak
To see what lay ahead;
My eyes grew wide in wonder
At the beauty I beheld.

Lush pastures beckoned to me,
Their hue a verdant green;
Still waters sparkled in the sun,
Fed by a silent stream.

I searched to find a place to start
My feet on their descent;
But jagged cliffs repelled me,
And my heart sank once again.

The sound of footsteps caught my ear,
I thought, who could this be?
I turned and saw a shepherd
Holding out his hand to me.

He led me to a hidden path
Worn smooth beneath his feet;
And when my footsteps faltered,
The shepherd carried me.

He laid me in a pasture
Among his flock of sheep;
My trip had left me weary,
And I soon was lost in sleep.

I slumbered through the balmy night
With hope inside my breast;
My struggles faded from me -
At last I'd found my rest.

When I awoke my head was full
Of thoughts of destiny;
I rose to find the shepherd,
For I sensed he held the key.

He led me to the water,
Its surface smooth as glass;
He bid me look into it
And the truth would come to pass.

I turned my vision downward
At the calm and silent sea;
And saw my own reflection
Staring strangely back at me.

With joy I started shouting that
I'd found myself at last!
But the shepherd quickly stopped me
When he raised his mighty staff.

He plunged the staff with anger
Into the once calm sea;
Causing waves and ripples
To distort my view of me.

Then suddenly the truth was clear:
It stilled my great confusion;
The vision mirrored back at me
Was merely an illusion.

I wasn't a reflection,
Yet I was the sky and sea;
I was the fertile pastures,
And the shepherd, too, was me.

I've finally gone full circle,
For the start and end are one;
This journey now has ended,
But another's just begun.

— Denise Dawn Anderson

All God's Children

WHEN I LOOK DOWN INTO MY LAP

At the rumbling ball of fur,
I think that God outdid Himself
When He created purr.

He gave to cats this special gift
That helps them to convey
The depth of their contentment
In such a vocal way.

Their kitty whiskers tickle,
And their softness I adore,
But all else is forgotten
When their motors start to roar!

No other creature on this earth
Has caused so much elation
By simply turning up the rate
Of their vocal cord vibration!

Now if I have offended you
With my single-minded ditty,
Please know I love all critters,
Not just my precious kitty.

It warms my heart completely
When dogs gaze up at me,
Or when they place a furry paw
Upon my bended knee.

And ducks and geese amuse me
With their waddle and their quack,
As do koala babies
When they ride on mama's back.

From the majesty of elephants
To squirrels as they scold,
I'm filled with joy and wonder
As their beauty I behold.

I've learned so much from animals,
They've taught me with their wisdom;
They've helped me to remember
That we're all God's little children.

Man has an obligation
To creatures great and small:
To respect them, to protect them,
And to love them, one and all.

— Denise Dawn Anderson

Clouds

I LIKE TO THINK OF PROBLEMS
As CLOUDS UP IN THE SKY,

Teaching us our lessons
As they go sailing by.

My favorite kind go scudding past
On Hermes' winged feet,
Never staying long enough
To signify defeat.

Others seem to represent
An army's proud formation,
With soldiers flashing thunderbolts
Across a wounded nation.

Dark and gray and ominous,
They wait impatiently
For just the moment to bestow
Their heavy load on me.

And if by chance I have the luck
To lead the clouds astray,
The fog rolls in to capture me
On yet another day.

But if I learn my lessons
From my discourse with the skies,
I'll see that all my problems
Are really blessings in disguise.

Beyond the clouds of dark despair
The skies are warm and bright
With all the crowning glory
Of the everlasting Light.

— Denise Daun Anderson

Rainbows

A LEPRECHAUN
ONCE TOLD ME,

As a secret to a friend,
That a pot of gold is hidden
At every rainbow's end.

Dreamers chase them often
As they while the hours away,
And imagine buried treasure
When they see a rainy day.

The rain clouds part, the sun peeks out,
And there so magically
Appears a brilliant rainbow
For all the world to see.

I used to search for rainbows,
A pot of gold to find,
But I always met with failure
For I searched with just my mind.

I finally looked inside me,
And I found that all this time
A rainbow truly did exist
Between God's heart and mine.

It's funny how my journey
Took me right back to the start,
Where I found the hidden treasure
Buried deep inside my heart.

— Denise Dawn Anderson

The Fairy's Visit

WHEN I WAS STILL
A LITTLE GIRL

Just seven years of age,
I noticed that a tooth of mine
Was acting very strange.

It used to make my smile look nice
And help me eat my food,
But when it started wiggling,
I thought, "How very rude!"

I watched it very closely,
Just to see what it would do,
But all it did was wobble
And make it hard for me to chew.

One day while eating dinner
Something didn't seem quite right -
I wondered what had happened
When I'd taken my last bite.

When it finally dawned on me
I let out quite a shout!
"You see," I told my family,
"My tooth has finally fallen out!"

It wasn't gross or slimy
As I thought that it might be,
It was smooth and white and pretty,
Like a shell beneath the sea.

I placed the tooth with care
Beneath my pillow that same night,
And someone must have been there
For I woke to such a sight!

Despite the gaping hole
A smile was bright upon my face,
For a fairy took my tooth
And left a coin there in its place!

When it comes to childhood traumas,
Losing teeth's my favorite one,
'Cause being visited by fairies
Is what I consider fun!

— *Denise Dawn Anderson*

Simple Beauty

SOME PEOPLE
SAY THE AMISH

Are as plain as they can be,
Yet I perceive such beauty
In their great simplicity.

I see quiet contemplation
In a little Amish face,
And all that they create by hand
Is filled with strength and grace.

Their quilts are hand-stitched beauty,
Their fields are sown with love,
And all they do throughout the day
Is for the One above.

Humility and family
Are expressions of their faith,
And working hard to help the rest
Is another honored trait.

You won't find excess finery
Throughout the Amish land,
For that which is most beautiful
Comes straight from God's own hand.

When you rid yourself of everything
That isn't truly you,
You'll find what's left is all that's best:
Your spirit shining through.

—Denise Daun Anderson

The Hidden Gift

WE OFTEN FEEL THE PRESENCE
OF THE ONE WE HOLD MOST DEAR

More strongly during Christmas
Than any other time of year.

It's in the children's faces
As their eyes grow large and bright
At the thought of Santa's visit
In the wee hours of the night.

It's in the sound of carols
Which bring tears to many eyes,
And the Hallelujah Chorus
Joined by angels from on high.

It's in our expectations
Of seeing friends from far away,
And renewing ties with family
On the blessed Savior's day.

These sights and sounds and feelings
Join to make us feel so blessed,
But in truth we don't need Christmas
For the joy to manifest.

If we take the time to step aside
From yuletide's hectic pace,
We'll find the holy presence
In a special, hidden place.

We don't need bows and glitter,
And all the outward fuss -
The most precious gift of Spirit
Is wrapped up inside of us.

— Denise Daun Anderson

Angel Song

SING WITH ME, MY CHILDREN,

Sing with Color, Light and Sound;
Sing with joyful heartstrings ~
Spread your loving all around.

Start with single melodies
Of simple thoughts and such;
Weave in smiles and laughter ~
A mother's gentle touch.

Add a slow crescendo
And a sudden change of pace;
A grace note of forgiveness ~
A sweet and radiant face.

Red and orange and yellow,
Green and blue and violet, too;
All of God's pure colors ~
Weave them brightly through and through.

From hushed angelic whispers
To chords of power and might;
Gently weave a theme throughout
Of Spirit's pure white Light.

Sing of earth and sky and sea,
And wind upon your face;
Of great majestic oak trees,
And of birches' leafy lace.

Sing of redwood forests,
And deserts parched and dry;
Of caves beneath the mother earth,
And rain clouds scudding by.

Sing of soft and rosy dawns
That sparkle on the dew;
And panoramic sunsets
Streaked with bold and vivid hues.

Sing of spring and summer days,
Of flitting butterflies;
Of fall and winter's cold embrace
Beneath a leaden sky.

Sing the brilliance of the sun
That makes our world so bright;
Sing the cycles of the moon,
And twinkling stars of night.

Sing of sweet abandon,
And of being young and free;
Of trust and dedication
And responsibility.

Sing of playful puppies
As they tumble on the lawn;
Of a watchful, wise old owl ~
A quiet spotted fawn.

Sing of fluffy kittens,
Of softly cooing doves;
And don't forget, my children,
Sing of universal love.

Sing through gales of laughter,
Through tragedy and tears;
Sing of dreams and visions,
And of all your greatest fears.

Sing of quiet inner strength,
Of doubts and questions, too;
Sing with pure acceptance,
Till the answers come to you.

Sing of newborn innocence,
Of aged, wrinkled face;
Sing of those who look like you,
And those of other race.

Honor all the differences
In countries near and far;
Acknowledge all the ways we see
How One we truly are.

Sing of great compassion
And of generosity;
Of simple acts of kindness
For those with special needs.

All souls in God's creation
Have a special part to sing;
For His eternal presence
Can be found in everything.

Share your voice with loved ones,
And with those who've done you wrong;
For in all of God's great choir,
They most need your loving song.

Instead of sounds of discord,
Sing a song of harmony;
Use the instruments of heaven
To create your symphony.

Use love and understanding,
Use grace and patience, too;
Use the wisdom of the angels
To begin your song anew.

Sing of calm surrender
To Spirit's higher plan;
Sing a song of brotherhood,
And peace throughout the land.

As you weave your lessons daily
Into your lifelong song,
You'll find that God's pure loving
Has been with you all along.

It showers you with brilliance,
And bursts of Light and Sound,
As you all become united
In the music all around.

So sing your song with clarity,
With faith, steadfast and true;
And you'll hear the heavenly chorus
Joining in your song with you.

As your voices come together
In songs of heartfelt love,
A rainbow fills the heavens
With glories from above.

Come with my, my children,
Let us sing the sacred tones
As we travel on together
To our true celestial home.

— *Denise Dawn Anderson*

Wondrous Love

QUIETLY IT ENTERS IN

On softly whispered sighs,
Accompanied not by heav'nly hosts,
Nor angels from on high.

In simple ways throughout our days
It weaves its way into
Our hearts and souls and memories;
It fills us through and through.

Each breath we take, each step we make
We're bathed in God's pure Light,
Though we sometimes feel forsaken,
We're always in plain sight.

Forever on we're safely kept
Within a warm embrace,
Like precious gems Light fills our lives
With love and peace and grace.

Rejoice in all the blessings
That our universe has bestowed,
Rejoice as well in all the ways
It strengthens weary souls.

Allow your heart to overflow
With the wonders of great love,
Then share that love with all you meet
Like an angel sends a dove.

— Denise Dawn Andersen

Tears

I USED TO HIDE MY TEARS AWAY
SO PEOPLE WOULDN'T SEE,

I thought that they were shameful,
Like a weaker part of me.

When something painful happened,
Especially to my heart,
I waited 'till I was all alone
To let the teardrops start.

And then one day a wiser soul
Explained her thoughts to me,
That sharing pain with others
Is a way to set it free!

Pain is life's great teacher,
A way to learn and grow,
And we can share the lessons
That the pain has helped us know.

The next time you are hurting,
And feeling really bad,
Take the time to look inside
To see what makes you sad.

You see, no matter what the pain,
There's a hidden blessing, too,
That shows a place of healing
Deep inside of you.

And when you share with others
This lesson you have learned,
It might be just the thing they need
The next time they get burned.

So let your tears fall freely
To cleanse the hurt away,
Like rain upon a thirsty earth
You'll see a brighter day.

— Denise Daun Anderson

Memories of a Mermaid

I MUST HAVE BEEN A MERMAID SOME TIME IN HISTORY,

For I've such a special kinship
With the mammals of the sea.

I love to watch the dolphins
As they frolic in the waves,
It takes me to a distant time
Of happy, peaceful days.

Their joy is quite apparent,
For they grin from ear to ear,
And their laughter plays like music
To those who chance to hear.

They have no room for hatred,
Though they've cause for great distrust,
For mankind through its blindness
Has abused them overmuch.

Sailors' logs are rife with tales
Of people lost at sea
Who are rescued from a certain death
By a dolphin's loving deed.

Forgotten are such stories
Of the angels of the sea -
We exploit these playful creatures
For our own destructive needs.

The whales are also friends of mine,
Those gentle, giant souls,
I recollect fond memories
From the days of long ago.

We'd dive among the ocean swells
In a game of hide 'n seek,
And wonder who would surface first
To take a hurried peek.

They'd often let me ride them
In a wet and joyful race,
Yet I never felt in danger
For their size belied their grace.

My heart is filled with sorrow
At the slaughter of my friends,
I only hope it's not too late
To reverse our killing trends.

It's true man has dominion
Over so-called lesser souls,
But can't we rule humanely
As we play our sovereign role?

If only we could learn to live
In peaceful harmony,
We might restore a precious trait
Called human dignity.

— Denise Daun Anderson

Loving

LISTEN,
CAN YOU HEAR IT?

It's the sound that loving makes.
Look closely, for it lives
In every form that Spirit takes.
It's hidden deep inside you,
And in all your friends and foes.
God's gift to all his children
Is everywhere you go.

Be still, and in the quietness
Your heart will find it knows
The answers to all questions,
And your joy soon overflows.
God's truth is like a beacon
Spreading Light for all our needs.
Fill your heart with its pure wisdom,
And use love in all your deeds.

The power is within you
To destroy or to create,
So make your choices wisely,
Stop and think before you hate.
Do only unto others
What you'd have them do to you.
Find your strength within your loving,
Let your Light come shining through.

— Denise Dawn Anderson